£3.55

The DANDY BOOK

ROLL UP! ROLL UP! LOTS OF FUN INSIDE.

Printed and Published in Great Britain by D. C. THOMSON &
CO., LTD., 185 Fleet Street, London EC4A 2HS.
© D. C. THOMSON & CO., LTD., 1989.
ISBN 0 85116 468 4

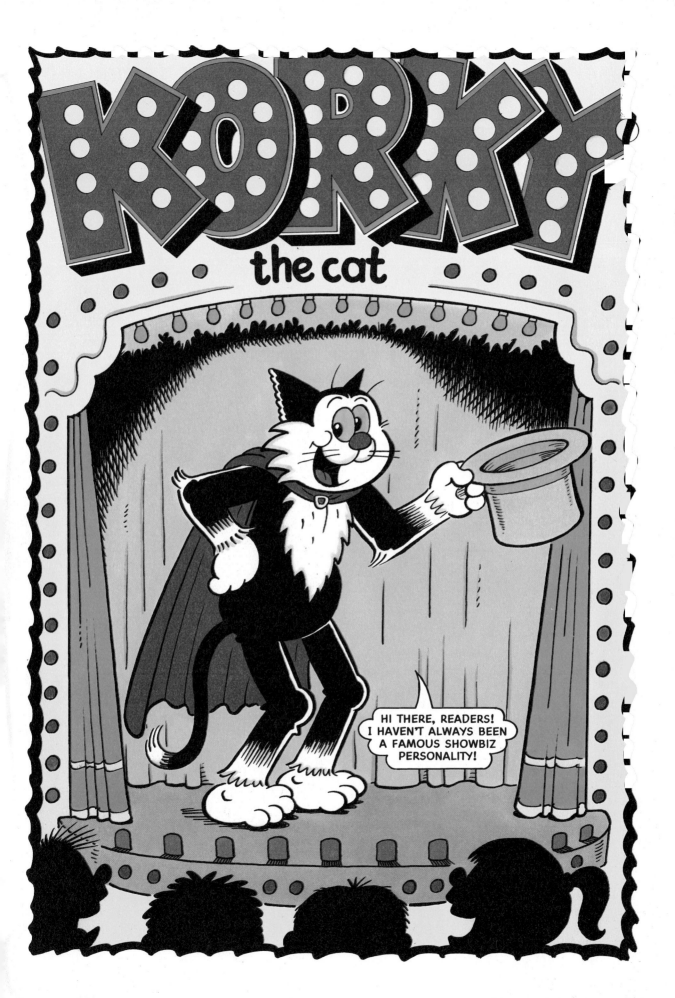

At one time life was hard as I waited for the breakthrough to stardom —

SHIVER!

SHAKE!

I'VE BEEN WAITING FOR TWO DAYS FOR THE KETTLE TO BOIL!

BRR!

HOW TO MAKE A GOOD IMPRESSION

SOON—

AH, THAT'S MUCH BETTER! NICE AND COSY NOW!

Things are starting to look up, Korky.

BUT—

NOT REALLY! I WAS ONLY PRACTISING MY IMPERSONATIONS!

IT SAYS HERE I NEED SOME PROPS!

PROPS

SO—

COO! IT'S MY FAVOURITE COMEDIAN, JASPER CARROT!

Cuddles and Dimples Sketch Pad

The sodden chums plodded back to Greytowers.

SHOWERS

MUTTER! THAT SNOBBY SKUNK WILL PAY FOR THIS.

Shortly —

IT JUST SO HAPPENS I HAVE A RADIO CONTROL UNIT TOO.

GOOD! HE'S STILL PLAYING WITH HIS PLANE.

Winker worked his radio unit —

— and took control of Jonathan's aircraft —

OH, MOTHER! MY BOMBER'S GONE BONKERS!

HELP! SAVE ME!

EEK!

CRASH!

N-NO! I'VE PRANGED THE SCHOOL COOK WITH OUR SUPPER.

Jonathan, of course, had his own chef —

BAH! HE'S GOT THE BETTER OF US AGAIN.

THE MILKSHAKE IS EXCELLENT. BUT THE JELLY IS ONE DEGREE TOO COLD.

After supper Winker and Tim decided to decorate their new potting shed dorm. Jonathan and his army of servants had taken over their old rooms.

THIS PLACE SHOULD SUIT YOU — IT SMELLS LIKE A PIG-STY.

GET LOST, DOSH!

POSTERS, EH! NOT A BAD IDEA.

Soon —

COME UP AND SEE MY NEW POSTERS, PEASANTS!

HMM! I WOULDN'T MIND SEEING WHAT YOU'VE DONE TO MY OLD ROOM.

Cuddles and Dimples Sketch Pad

Dinah Mo's Fairy Tales

The Pied Piper of Hamelin

EEK! A MOUSE!

DON'T WORRY, MUM. I'LL GET RID OF YOUR RODENTS!

TCH! DON'T BELIEVE THAT BOOK, MO. THAT'S ONLY A FAIRY TALE!

THE PIED PIPER OF HAMELIN

MUNCH

DRONE! GROAN!♫!

OOH! WHAT A DIN!

But —

OKAY! WE GIVE IN. C'MON, LADS. WE CAN'T LIVE WITH THIS DIN!

YOWL!♫ ♫GROAN!♫ BLARE!

COME BACK THE PROCLAIMERS

c

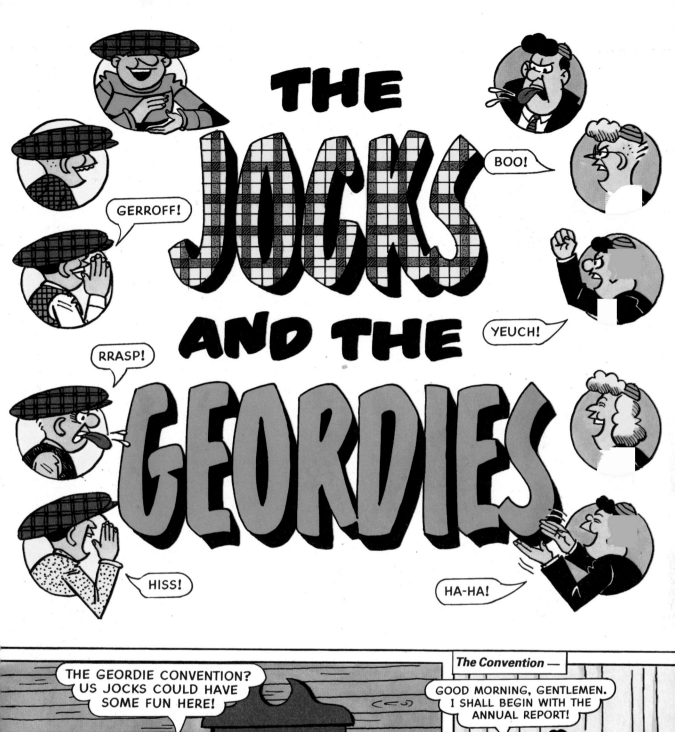

THE JOCKS AND THE GEORDIES

Outside —

JOCKS BIFFED — 372.
JOCKS THUMPED — 269 . . .

THIS'LL RUMBLE THEM UP!

GO GET 'EM, BOY!

JOCKS BASHED — 427 . . .
AN OVERALL INCREASE OF
TWELVE PER CENT THERE.

OOYAH!
THUD! BUTT! THUMP!
ARRGH! OW!

LOVELY.

ER . . . SPECIAL MENTION
MUST GO TO EGBERT, WHO
SINGLE-HANDED, SABOTAGED
THE JOCK PORRIDGE
FACTORY.

QUIETLY DOES IT!

THIS'LL HEAT UP THEIR
BREAKFASTS — OOPS!

Meanwhile —

ALI HA-HA

Mustapha Phag, leader of the 40 thieves.

Dinah Mo's Fairy Tales

Rapunzel

LETTER BOX
HAIR MAIL
ONLY

MIND YOU, THIS BEATS BORING OLD STAIRS.

I'VE BROUGHT YOUR BIKE BACK, RAPUNZEL. YOU SHOULD COME AND HAVE A LOOK.

OKAY, BUT WE WON'T BOTHER WITH THE HAIR.

WE'LL TAKE THE LIFT.

PRESS

WELL I NEVER!

And —

GRR! MO! MY BIKE! I'LL SPIFFLICATE YOU!

RACE!

I DOUBT IT!

WHY'S THAT?

COS RAPUNZEL, RAPUNZEL, I'VE LET OUT YOUR AIR!

BAH! MY BLOOMIN' TYRES ARE FLAT!

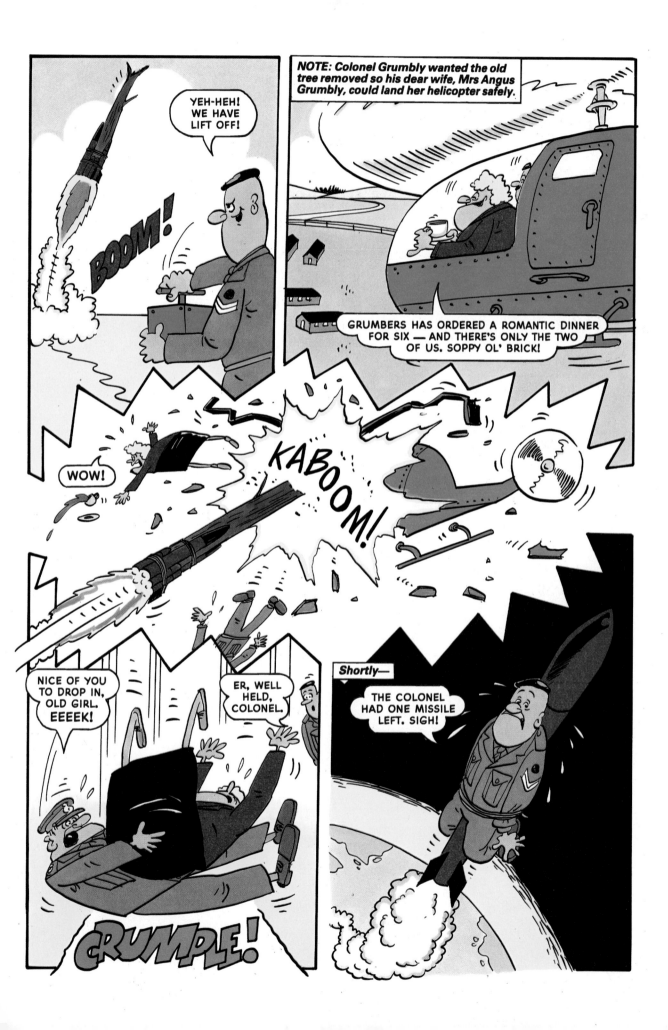

SMASHER'S SMASHATHON

BRASSNECK

THE AMAZING METAL BOY!

MY METAL PAL, BRASSNECK, HAS LOTS OF DIFFERENT HEADS!

HE'S EVEN GOT A HEAD THAT LOOKS LIKE ME!

I KEEP IT WITH ALL MY OTHER HEADS!

WE LIKE BODY-BUILDING! I USE WEIGHTS!

I USE A SPANNER!

BRASSNECK HAS SPECIAL SPRINTING PARTS TOO!

E

IT'S SATURDAY NIGHT AND THERE'S A SQUARE-DANCE AT DUDGE CITY TOWN HALL! I CAN HARDLY WAIT!

MUST GET MYSELF SPRUCED UP...

I NEED A SHAVE.

UNDER THE ARMS FIRST...

...THEN MY CHIN!

DOGGONE IT! IT'S GONE OUT!

PHUT!

And so —

MAY I HAVE THE HONOUR, MISS ISA?

WHY I'D BE DELIGHTED, DAN.

I LOVE A COYOTE TROT.

But —

AARGH! MY HAIR!

IF IT AIN'T YOUR SIZE 20 BOOTS THAT DO THE DAMAGE IT'S YOUR CHIN.

THERE, THERE. DON'T CRY, ISA.

I JUST AIN'T CUT OUT FOR DANCIN'!

THE REST OF THE GASWORKS GANG

WOO-HOO! GET A LOAD OF THE SWEET LITTLE GIRLIE!

CISSY!

NOT AT ALL! I'M BEING FEMININE.

US GIRLS ARE VERY GRACEFUL! GOOD AT BALLET!

SEE?

WHIRRR!

LIKE MY NEW PERFUME?

PARFUM DE PIGLET!

UGH! WHAT A GUFF!

RATTLE! RATTLE!

DOOF!

YEAH! BUT WE BE VERY TOUGH.

EEK! THE ROYAL BONCE!

TINY KNIGHTS NEED ONLY SMALL SUITS OF ARMOUR. THAT BE CHEAP, SIRE.

HMMM!

AND WE CAN PUT THREE OF THEM ON EACH CHARGER. SO WE WON'T NEED SO MANY HORSES.

CHEAPER STILL! YES, THEY'LL DO!

Enter that black rascal, Baron Howl, on his turbo charger—

MORNING, KING RAT! I CHALLENGE YOUR NITS, I MEAN KNIGHTS, TO A DUEL.

SLAP!

GADZOOKS! ANOTHER BONK ON YE ROYAL BONCE.

Dinah Mo's Fairy Tales

THE THREE BEARS

At Brownie camp —

ERK! WHO'S BEEN SLEEPING IN MY BED?

YAWN!

AND WHO'S BEEN SLEEPING IN MY BED?

AND WHO'S . . .

WHAT'RE YOU LOT ON ABOUT? I HAVEN'T MADE THE BEDS YET!

BAH!

GOLDILOCK'S and the THREE BEARS

WHO'S BEEN EATING MY PORRIDGE?

WILL YOU LOT BE PATIENT? I HAVEN'T FINISHED MAKING IT!

SPLOT!

BAH! WE'VE HAD ENOUGH, MO. AND YOUR LOCKS AREN'T GOLDEN!

DO THE CHORES WHILE WE'RE AT NEEDLEWORK!

TCH! IT'S TIME WE TAUGHT MO A LESSON!

WHO'S BEEN READING OUR FAIRY-TALE!

ULP! WHO'S THAT?

AND YOU HAVEN'T DONE THE CHORES!

YERK! THREE BEARS!

I'LL DO MY CHORES! JUST DON'T HURT ME, PLEASE!

FASTER, MO. FASTER!

GUESS WHAT WE MADE AT NEEDLEWORK CLASS, READERS?

AHEM! I PUT A FILE IN DAD'S CAKE.

Bo visits Blueberry farm—

HIYA, MISTER!

YOU'VE SCARED MY 'ORSE, YOU 'AVE!

JUST BORROWING YOUR FILE FOR A WHILE.

I WANT MY MUMMY!

WHINE!

Brains is at work in the garden shed—

HAMMER! THUMP!

I HOPE MY LAD'S NOT MAKING ANOTHER ATOMIC STINK BOMB.

I'VE INVENTED A LASER POWERED SUPER FILE.

WHIRRR!

SNEAKER

Cuddles and Dimples Sketch Pad

Dinah Mo's Fairy Tales
LITTLE RED RIDING HOOD

BLACK BOB

CHAMPION OF CHAMPIONS

ANY SIGN OF THAT MISSING RAM, ANDREW?

Andrew Glenn, Scotland's top sheep-dog handler, was helping neighbouring farmer Geoff Billingham to gather his sheep! At his side, as always, was his faithful collie, Black Bob.

AYE! I CAN SEE THE OLD RASCAL ON A ROCKY LEDGE UP ON SCAR PIKE!

A sharp whistle from Glenn sent Bob in pursuit of the fugitive ram!

The clever collie soon had the ram cornered, but the shepherd was worried in case it slipped off the narrow ledge.

THAT'LL DO, BOB! LEAVE IT!

Andrew Glenn decided to use cunning to capture the runaway ram.

THIS IS A TRICK I LEARNED FROM BIG JOE MCROBERTS AT FINGLAND.

HERE'S THE ROPE!

Wearing a sheepskin, Bob crept closer to the unsuspecting ram!

On a low hissed order from his master, the wily collie dropped the rope over the grazing ram's horns.

WELL DONE, BOB. NOW I CAN PULL HIM IN LIKE A SALMON ON A LINE.

HE WON'T GIVE YOU ANY MORE TROUBLE NOW, GEOFF!

The Billinghams had only recently moved into Tweedhope Croft, and Glenn was helping them to round up and check on their flock of sheep.

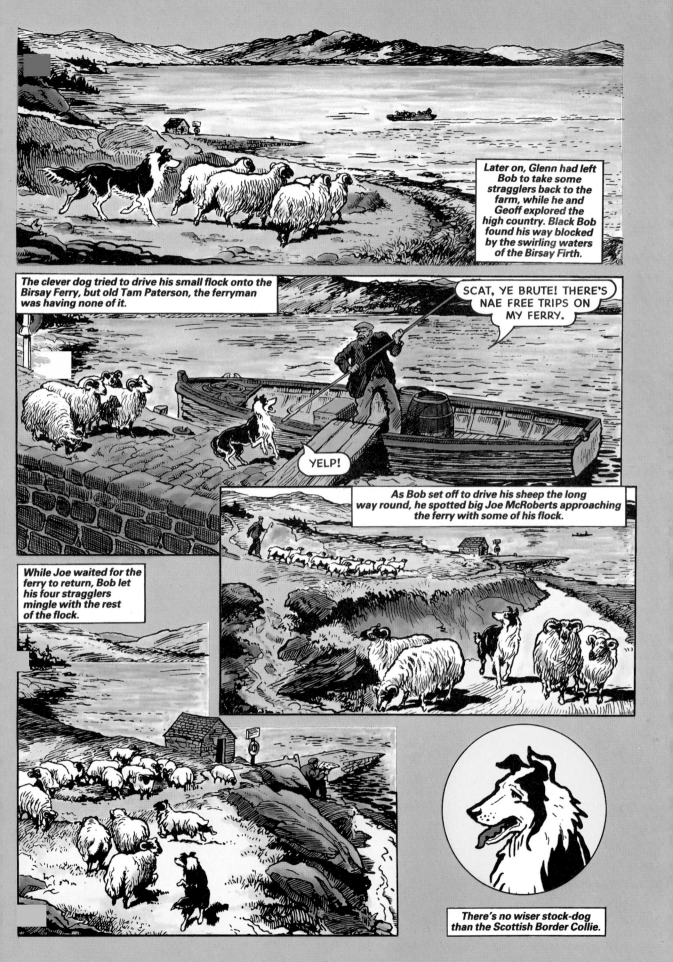

Later on, Glenn had left Bob to take some stragglers back to the farm, while he and Geoff explored the high country. Black Bob found his way blocked by the swirling waters of the Birsay Firth.

The clever dog tried to drive his small flock onto the Birsay Ferry, but old Tam Paterson, the ferryman was having none of it.

SCAT, YE BRUTE! THERE'S NAE FREE TRIPS ON MY FERRY.

YELP!

As Bob set off to drive his sheep the long way round, he spotted big Joe McRoberts approaching the ferry with some of his flock.

While Joe waited for the ferry to return, Bob let his four stragglers mingle with the rest of the flock.

There's no wiser stock-dog than the Scottish Border Collie.

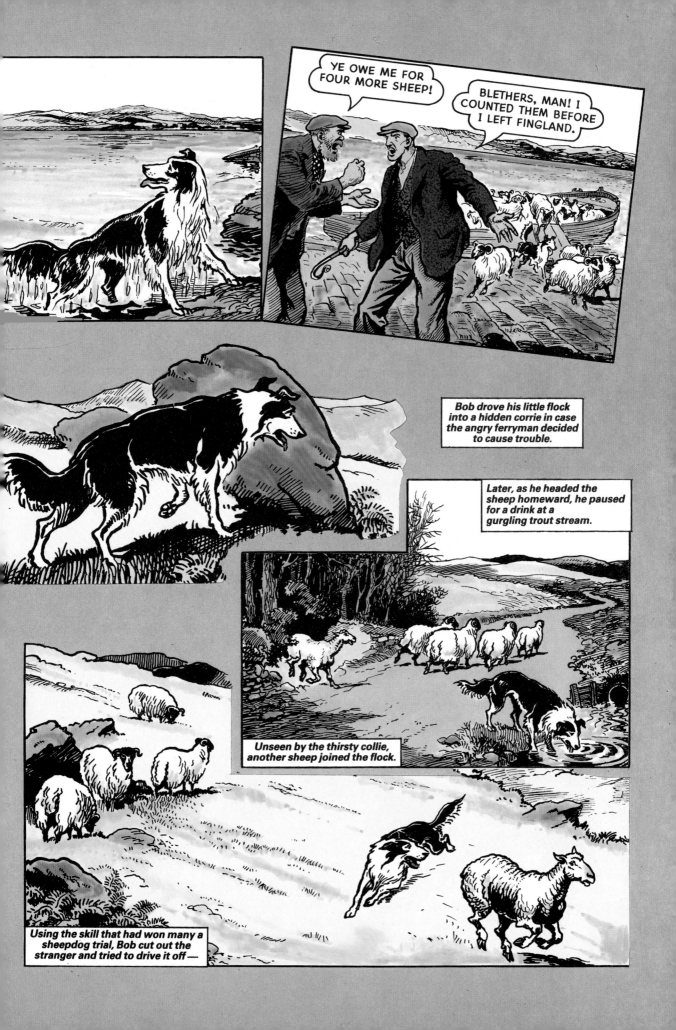

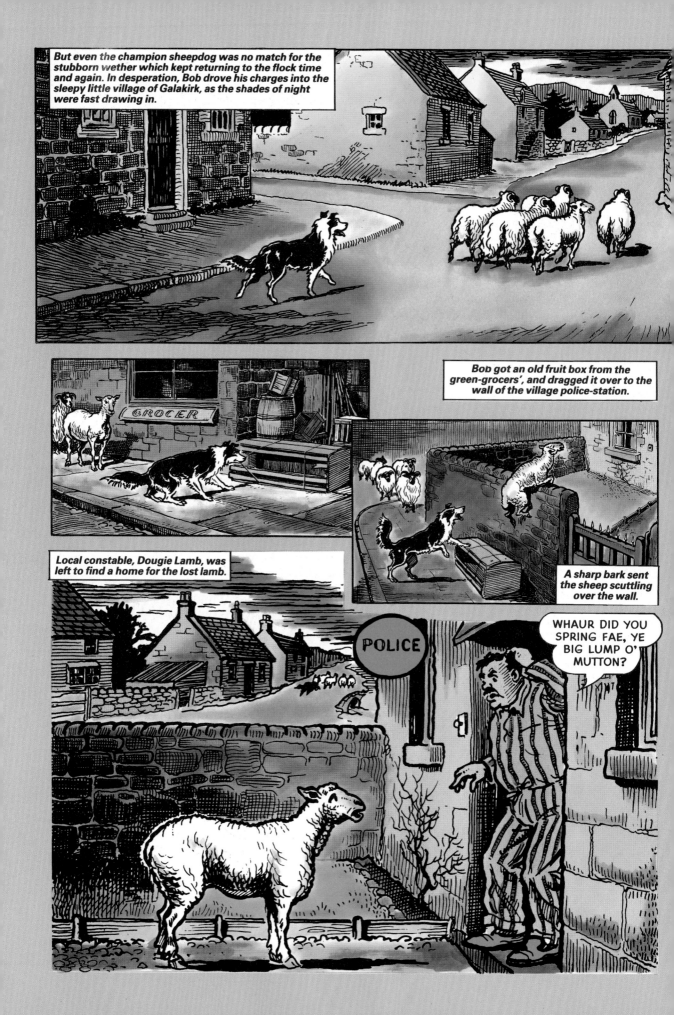

The powerful old tractor soon pulled the shepherd clear of the clinging embrace of the treacherous quick-sand.
Then they used the rope to pull in the box that had almost cost the big shepherd his life.

IT'S YOUR TOOL BOX, GEOFF!

This would be a godsend as they set about rebuilding Tweedhope Croft.

Resolutely, the Billinghams faced up to the challenge.

IT LOOKS BAD JUST NOW, BUT WITH A BIT OF WORK WE'LL HAVE THE OLD CROFT LOOKING BETTER THAN EVER!

In the best traditions of the hill-country, Glenn and Bob rallied round to help their stricken neighbours. All in a day's work for the big shepherd and his champion sheepdog.

DRAGONS HAVE HOLIDAYS TOO, YOU KNOW.

GEORGE
AND THE
DRAGON

TCH! I'M NOT GOING IF IT'S RAINING.

HAR! HAR! WHAT A DIM REPTILE.

SIGH!

SCARED OF A LITTLE RAIN HE IS.

LOIKS!

THAT THUNDER STORM HAS CLEARED THE AIR.

I HATE ENGLISH WEATHER! MUTTER! MUTTER!

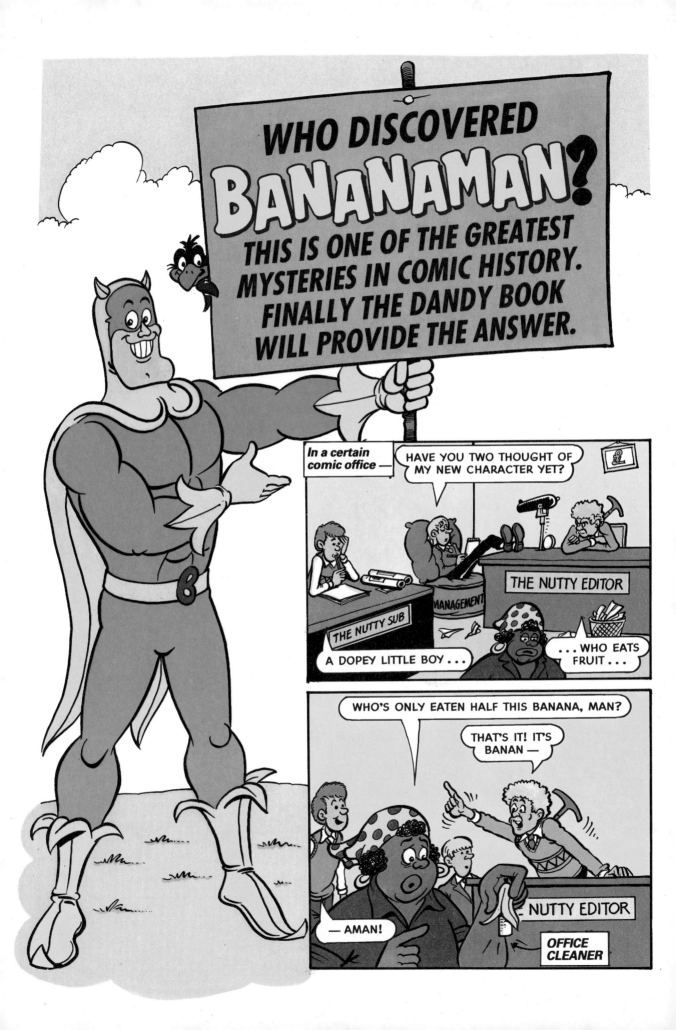

OKAY, THAT'S ENOUGH! SORRY, READERS! YOU WERE PROMISED THE TRUTH ABOUT ME AND YOU'RE NOT GETTING IT!

R.R.RIP!

IT ALL STARTED YEARS AGO WHEN I WAS NOT A LITTLE ERIC BUT A BABY ERIC . . .

LIES! ALL LIES I TELL YOU!

DIARY OF BANANAMAN

At the maternity-hospital —

HE'S A HUNGRY LITTLE MITE, NURSE.

YES! MOST UNUSUAL FOR A NEW-BORN BABY TO HAVE SUCH A SET OF CHOMPERS.

CHOMP! CHOMP!

BUT I WOULDN'T WORRY. HE SEEMS TO BE TAKING HIS MILK QUITE NATURALLY.

Meanwhile, nearby —

STOP HIM! HE'S STOLEN A SUPPLY OF SATURNIUM!

GENERAL BLIGHT— A NASTY PERSON!

DANGER RADIATION

KITCHING

I'LL HIDE IN HERE!

AW—NAUGHTY MAN!

THIS SATURNIUM IS ALL I NEED TO MAKE MY NEW DESTRUCT-A-RAY.

WHERE'S HE GONE?

HE MUST HAVE GONE ANOTHER WAY!

EXCELLENT! I'VE LOST THEM.

I'LL HAVE TO DISGUISE THE SATURNIUM AND MYSELF IF I WANT TO GET OUT OF THE HOSPITAL.

FRANK FURTER WILL NOW SING— COME FRY WITH ME!

FRANK FURTER →

And so —

I'M THE FOOD NURSE, WHAT DID YOU ORDER, DEAR?

BABY ERIC'S PAW

S'MPLE!!

TRIPE AND ONIONS WITH RASPBERRY RIPPLE.

Suddenly —

FOOM!

GURGLE-GLOOP!

WH-WHAT HAPPENED?

YIKES! MY NANA'S BEEN NICKED.

TIME I WASN'T HERE.

DON'T WORRY, MUM. I'LL STOP HIM.

B'MAN LEARNT TO SPEAK VERY QUICKLY:— Ed.

OUT OF MY WAY.

OOF!

THAT MULTI-GYM I STOLE MUST BE PAYING OFF — I FEEL LIKE I'M FLYING.

THAT'S BECAUSE YOU ARE, YOU HORRIBLE VILLAIN YOU.

ERK! I'VE BEEN LIFTED.